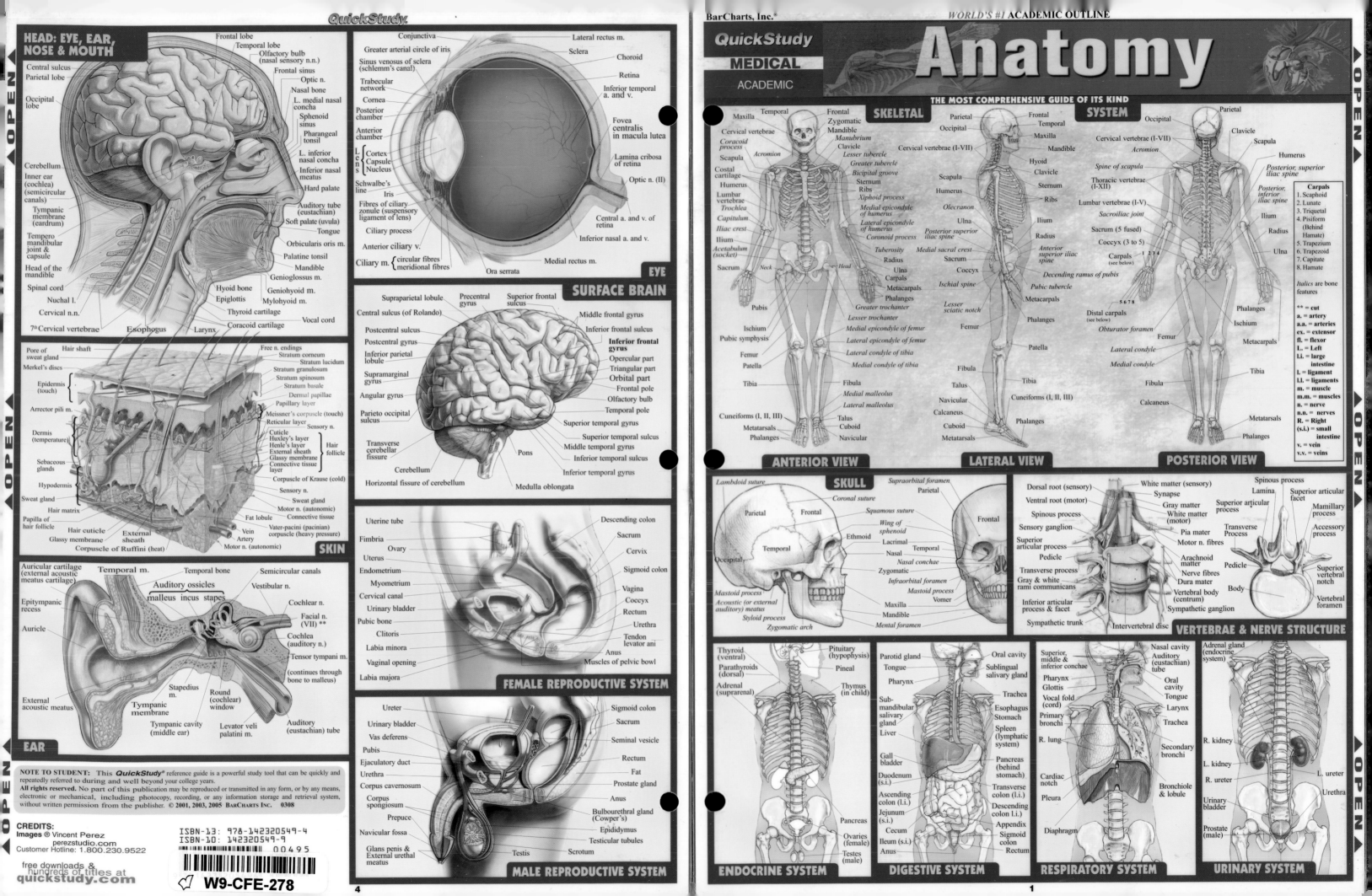

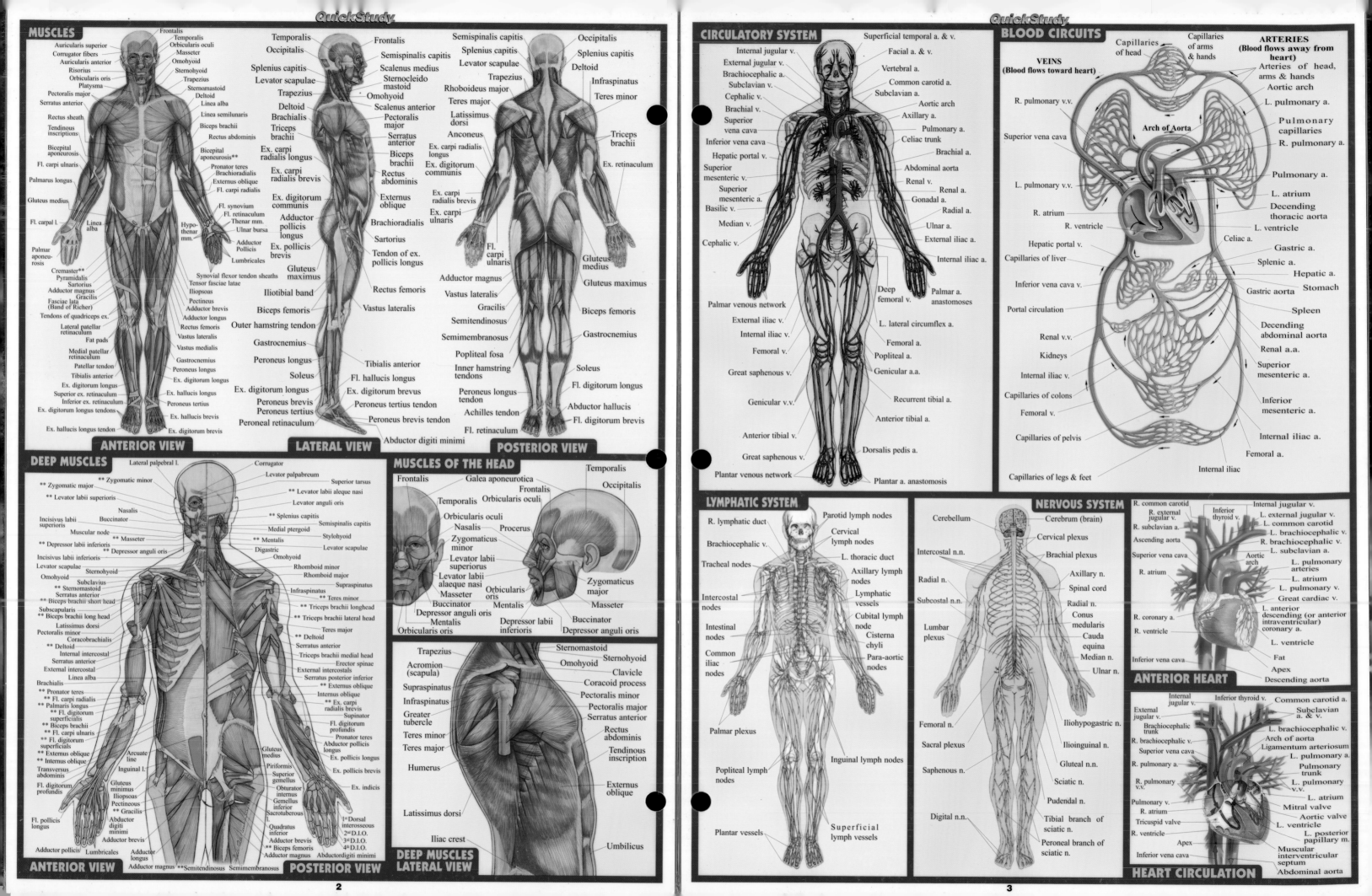

MUSCLES

ANTERIOR VIEW

LATERAL VIEW

POSTERIOR VIEW

DEEP MUSCLES

ANTERIOR VIEW

POSTERIOR VIEW

MUSCLES OF THE HEAD

DEEP MUSCLES LATERAL VIEW

CIRCULATORY SYSTEM

BLOOD CIRCUITS

VEINS
(Blood flows toward heart)

ARTERIES
(Blood flows away from heart)

Arch of Aorta

LYMPHATIC SYSTEM

NERVOUS SYSTEM

ANTERIOR HEART

HEART CIRCULATION